C000269512

GCSE
Science
HIGHER COURSEWORK
STUDENT'S GUIDE

Bob McDuell

EDUCATIONAL

First published 1997
Reprinted 1998

Letts Educational
Schools and Colleges Division
9–15 Aldine Street
London W12 8AW
0181 740 2270

Text: © Bob McDuell
Design and illustrations © BPP (Letts Educational) Ltd 1997

Design and page layout: Moondisks Ltd, Cambridge

British Library Cataloguing-in-Publication Data
A CIP record for this book is available from the British Library

ISBN 1 84085 1457

Printed and bound in Great Britain

Letts Educational is the trading name of BPP (Letts Educational) Ltd

Contents

Introduction

This Letts GCSE Science Coursework Student's book has been specially designed to help you understand how Sc1 assessment works. It is for students taking:

- GCSE Science: Double Award
- GCSE Science: Single Award
- GCSE Separate Sciences – Physics, Chemistry, Biology

First write your name and teaching group on page 5.

Now read the '**A close look at Sc1**' section on pages 6 to 8 as this describes the way Science is divided into different Attainment Targets and looks in detail at Sc1 – the investigating skills it covers, the way marks are allocated and how important its skills are in your whole examination.

We advise you to work through the units in order studying the example questions carefully as this is where you can gain valuable advice on how to improve your investigative skills and go on to score higher marks. Your teacher will be able to help you check your answers.

It is important to use this book at the same time that you carry out investigations in the GCSE Science Coursework book so that you can build on your knowledge as you complete each new investigation.

We hope that this Student's book and the Coursework book will help you to achieve your desired performance in Sc1, and increase your enjoyment of investigating Science.

The following quotation confirms the importance of investigation to furthering the study of Science:

Comparing predictions with reality is the way Science makes progress.

BBC Science Correspondent, May 1997,
on a computer model being developed to
confirm the origins of the Universe

Getting your best results with Sc1

A course booklet designed to help you make progress in Sc1

Name

Teaching group

A close look at Sc1

The following table shows the percentage of marks allocated to each Attainment Target for Science: Double Award, Science: Single Award and Separate Sciences for GCSE.

	Attainment Target 1	Attainment Target 2 – Biology	Attainment Target 3 – Chemistry	Attainment Target 4 – Physics
	Sc1	Sc2	Sc3	Sc4
Science: Double Award	25%	25%	25%	25%
Science: Single Award	25%	25%	25%	25%
Science: Biology	25%	75%		
Science: Chemistry	25%		75%	
Science: Physics	25%			75%

Each syllabus allocates 25% of the total marks to Sc1. The Attainment Target is called **Experimental and Investigative Science** and gets you to apply your knowledge and understanding of Sc2, Sc3 and Sc4 and so develop your practical and investigational skills.

During years 10–11 there will be opportunities for your teacher to assess your Sc1 performance in four **skill areas**.

- **Skill Area P – Planning experiments.**
- **Skill Area O – Obtaining evidence.** Carrying out experiments and recording the results.
- **Skill Area A – Analysing evidence and drawing conclusions.** Looking at the results, plotting graphs and drawing conclusions.
- **Skill Area E – Evaluating the evidence.** Looking at the experiment and checking its validity and suggesting ways it could have been done better.

There is no limit to the number of times you can be assessed. With certain restrictions, explained on page 28, only your **best mark** in each skill area counts towards the final mark.

Skill Area P – maximum of 8 marks

Skill Area O – maximum of 8 marks

Skill Area A – maximum of 8 marks

Skill Area E – maximum of 6 marks   **Total 30 marks**

This is then doubled to 60 marks and a mark (1, 2 or 3) added depending upon the quality of your spelling, punctuation and grammar.

Marks	E: Evaluating evidence — Evaluating my work
2 marks	I can say something about how well my plan has worked.
4 marks	↑ plus… I can say how accurate my results are and if my experiment can be improved.
6 marks	↑ plus… I can explain if my evidence is good enough to support my conclusion. I can suggest improvements to obtain better results.

Marks	P: Planning — Planning my work	O: Obtaining evidence — Collecting my data	A: Analysing evidence — Making my conclusions
2 marks	I can plan something to investigate.	I can use equipment safely and take some readings or measurements.	I can show what I have found out.
4 marks	↑ plus… I know that my plan is a fair test, and can choose the right equipment to use.	↑ plus… I can take a series of useful readings or measurements, and I can record them carefully.	↑ plus… By using diagrams, charts or simple graphs, I can show if there is a pattern in what I have found.
6 marks	↑ plus… Using scientific ideas I can decide which are the most important factors. I can say what readings I will need to take, and how many of them I will need.	↑ plus… I can make careful and accurate readings or measurements and record them clearly. I can repeat my observations and measurements if this will help.	↑ plus… I can use my scientific knowledge and the information from my diagrams, charts or graphs to help me make a conclusion.
8 marks	↑ plus… I can use detailed scientific ideas in my plan to help me to get reliable results. I have used details of any information which helped me to plan.	↑ plus… I can use equipment skilfully to obtain high quality results.	↑ plus… I can use detailed scientific ideas to explain my conclusion. I can say how my results link back to my planning.

In marking your investigations, your teacher uses a set of **criteria**. Your work is matched to the criteria. The table on page 3, shows the criteria your teacher uses, but written in a simpler language to help you to understand them. You will notice that statements for Skill Areas P, O and A are given at 2 marks, 4 marks, 6 marks and 8 marks. For Skill Area E, statements are given at 2 marks, 4 marks and 6 marks. If your piece of work is good enough to get more than 2 marks for planning, but not good enough for 4 marks, your teacher will give the work 3 marks. If the criteria for 6 or 8 marks contain two statements, you must achieve both statements to be awarded the mark. For example, for a mark of 8 for Skill Area A, you have to use detailed scientific ideas to explain the conclusion, and say how your results link back to your original planning. Failing to link back to the planning would restrict your marks to 6 or 7.

Whole investigations and part investigations

From 1998 Sc1 can include part investigations as well as whole investigations. A whole investigation is an experiment where you do the planning, carry it out, process the results and evaluate the experiment. You get a mark for each of the Skill Areas.

If your teacher gave you a detailed plan for you to carry out, the experiment could be used to assess Skill Areas O, A and E, but not P. It would be, therefore, a part investigation. If your teacher demonstrated an experiment before giving you a set of results, this could be used to assess you in Skill Areas A and E. Your teacher could ask you to plan an experiment which is never carried out. This could be used to assess Skill Area P.

In all syllabuses at least one mark has to come from a whole investigation. At least one whole investigation must, therefore, be done.

We are now going to look at each Skill Area separately and find out what you have to do to achieve good marks in each. We will use a few practical examples to help us. In some cases they may be easier than the one you would use in practice. However, they illustrate the important points.

Skill Area P

Planning experimental procedures

There are key points you need to know before you start planning.

- When confronted with a task, you have to use scientific knowledge and understanding from the appropriate sections of Sc2, Sc3 and Sc4 to put the task into a form which you can investigate.

- Sometimes preliminary work may help. For example, use a preliminary experiment to find the best range within which measurements are to be made. Evidence of thorough preliminary work is one way of scoring very high planning marks.

- Whenever you are planning you should look to see if you can make a **prediction**. Predictions are not essential, but making a prediction is often an important step in planning. A prediction without any scientific knowledge and understanding is only a guess. Back up any prediction with knowledge and understanding. You will often find this in a textbook, e.g. Letts *GCSE Science Classbook*. Do not copy out whole sections, but select appropriate parts.

- You should consider how many observations or measurements will be needed and you must think about the range of measurements you are planning.

- You must select apparatus, equipment and materials carefully to ensure your experiment is safe.

- It is important to understand the term **variable**. A variable is a factor that is measured or controlled. A variable that you can change is called an **independent variable**. A variable over which you have no control is called a **dependent variable**. If you carry out a rate of reaction experiment and vary the temperature, the time of the reaction will vary. The temperature, over which you have control, is the independent variable and time is a dependent variable.

In many cases there are a number of variables that have a bearing on an experimental situation. Some variables, called **key variables**, are particularly important. You should identify key variables and consider how to control them.

Sometimes, especially in Biology assessments, situations are very complex and there are many variables operating, and controlling these variables is very difficult.

Variables may also be classified as **continuous** or **discrete**. A discrete variable has only certain values. For example, a simple experiment to find the number of indigestion tablets required to neutralise a given volume of acid would give answers of 1, 2, 3 or similar. There are no possible intermediate values. If the same acid solution is titrated with an alkali, the value obtained would not necessarily be a whole number, but could be a value such as 1.7 cm^3 or 2.5 cm^3 and is a **continuous variable**.

You do not need to consider two or more different factors, and you do not have to compare the effect that one factor has with the effect the other has.

We will now consider an example.

You have three beakers made of different materials – copper, plastic and glass. **Plan an experiment to compare how quickly hot water in each beaker cools**.

Why does the water in each beaker cool?
Most of the energy is lost by conduction through the walls of the beaker. In thermal conduction energy is passed from particle to adjacent particle (see Letts *Science Classbook*, pages 304–5). You could find values for the thermal conductivity of the three materials in a databook. (Plastic 0.04, glass 1.1 and copper 403 – arbitrary units.)

On the basis of this knowledge and understanding, you could predict that the water would cool faster in the copper beaker than the glass beaker, and faster in the glass beaker than the plastic beaker. This is your **prediction**.

Your prediction applies providing you carry out a **fair test**. This means starting with the same volume of hot water, at approximately the same temperature, stirring in the same way etc. The only thing you are changing is the material used to make the beaker.

beaker
crystallising dish
crucible and lid
flask
burette
gas syringe
measuring cylinder
funnel
Petri dish and lid
teat (or dropping)
 pipette
test tube
watch glass
trough
pestle and mortar
pipette
thistle funnel
evaporating basin
gas jar and lid

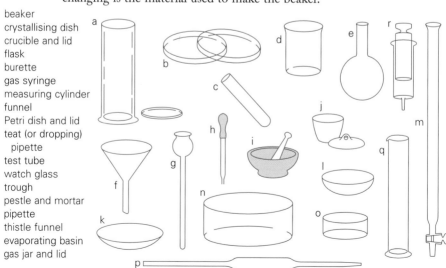

Figure 1

Q 1.1 Next, you have to choose your equipment. Figs 1 and 2 show a large number of pieces of apparatus. Write down the correct name for each piece of apparatus.

Figure 1:

a _____   b _____

c _____   d _____

e _____   f _____

g _____   h _____

i _____   j _____

k _____   l _____

m _____   n _____

o _____   p _____

q _____   r _____

Figure 2:

a _____   b _____

c _____   d _____

e _____   f _____

g _____   h _____

i _____   j _____

k _____   l _____

tripod
pipe-clay
  triangle
test tube
  holders
tongs
boss
retort stand
gauze
spatula
test tube rack
combustion
  spoon
clamp
wooden (or
  burette)
  stand

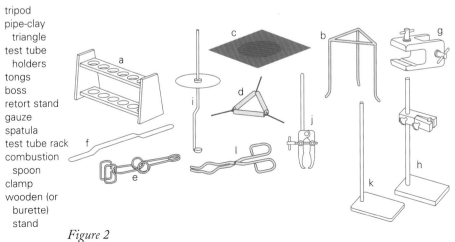

Figure 2

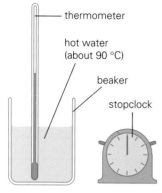

Figure 3

For our experiment we will use the apparatus shown in Figure 3.

Schools often have different thermometers measuring different temperature ranges. Three common ones are:

A 0 °C to 360 °C thermometer with 2 °C divisions.

B 0 °C to 50 °C thermometer with 0.1 °C divisions.

C –10 °C to 110 °C thermometer with 1 °C divisions.

Q 1.2 Which thermometer would you choose for this investigation?

_____

Why did you choose this one?

_____

_____

A preliminary experiment might help you to decide how many minutes to leave the beaker to cool. Try the copper beaker and take the temperature every couple of minutes. Preliminary experiments suggest seven minutes is sufficient.

Here is your plan:

1   Add 100 cm³ of hot water to the copper beaker you are using from a plastic measuring jug or plastic measuring cylinder.

2   Put the thermometer in the water.

3   After half a minute, take the temperature.
    Do not take the thermometer out of the water.

4   Take the temperature again every half minute for seven minutes.

5   Repeat the experiment with the glass and plastic beakers.

On page 22 the results of this experiment are processed and evaluated.

2 Skill Area O

Obtaining evidence

There are key points you need to know before you start making observations and measurements.

▓ This Skill Area requires you to use apparatus safely and skilfully. If you are not sure how to use a piece of apparatus, do not be afraid to ask for advice. You *must* wear goggles when handling chemicals.

▓ Record your observations and measurements as soon as you make them. Don't think you will remember them! You do not have to use a table, but a well-planned table is usually the best way to record the results. Design your table before you start.

▓ Look critically at the observations and measurements as you make them. Take them again if you are not satisfied. You may not be able to repeat them later.

Here are the results for the cooling of the three beakers.

Time/minutes	Temperature of water in glass beaker/°C	Temperature of water in plastic beaker/°C	Temperature of water in copper beaker/°C
0.5	80.0	79.0	78.0
1.0	77.0	76.0	75.0
1.5	75.0	74.5	72.0
2.0	74.0	73.0	70.0
2.5	73.0	72.0	68.0
3.0	72.0	70.5	66.5
3.5	70.5	69.0	64.0
4.0	69.0	67.5	63.0
4.5	68.0	66.0	62.0
5.0	67.0	65.0	61.0
5.5	66.0	64.0	59.0
6.0	65.0	63.0	57.5
6.5	64.0	61.5	56.0
7.0	63.0	60.0	55.0

Figure 4: 77.5 °C is between 77° and 78°.

> **Q 2.1** Notice that each temperature reading is taken to the nearest 0.5 °C. Although the thermometer has 1° divisions, it is possible to read it to the nearest 0.5° (see Figure 4).
>
> Why was the temperature of the water not taken after 0 minutes, i.e. at the start of the experiment?
>
> _____

Making observations

It is important when making observations, to make *all* the possible observations and not just some of them. All changes have some significance, although you might not realise exactly what until later. It was often the tiniest detail, which Dr Watson – and some of us – would not notice, which enabled Sherlock Holmes to solve the case. He could then say, 'Elementary, my dear Watson'.

For example, in a simple experiment where a solid substance is heated in a test tube, you might look for:

- changes in colour
- changes in state, e.g. solid ⇒ liquid, or solid ⇒ gas
- gas evolved
- formation of a precipitate
- temperature changes showing exothermic or endothermic reactions
- crackling noises when a solid decomposes.

A sample of sulphur heated in a test tube can produce at least ten observations.

1 Sulphur melts at a low temperature.

2 It forms a pale amber-coloured liquid.

3 The liquid is free-flowing (mobile) at this stage.

4 On further heating, the liquid goes darker in colour.

5 The liquid eventually turns black.

6 At this stage the liquid is difficult to pour (viscous)

7 The liquid starts to boil.

8 The sulphur catches alight.

9 It burns with a pale blue flame.

10 It produces a choking smell.

If you look at these observations, you should notice how detailed they are. Do not say something is yellow, say it is amber yellow, canary yellow, dark yellow – anything other than just yellow. Get used to describing a colour with two words rather than one, e.g. blood red rather than red.

Q 2.2 How many other descriptions of yellow can you think of? Make a list.

_____

How many descriptions of the colour green can you think of? Write some down.

_____

How many descriptions of the colour blue can you think of? Write some down.

_____

The secret of achieving good marks for observing as part of Skill Area O is to give full and detailed observations. Pretend you are explaining to somebody who is at the other end of a telephone what happens. Do not forget to report even trivial observations – often these become important when they are put in the correct context.

Q 2.3 Figure 5 shows drawings of four types of woodlouse. Ignoring differences in size, write down **one way** each of them is different from the other three.

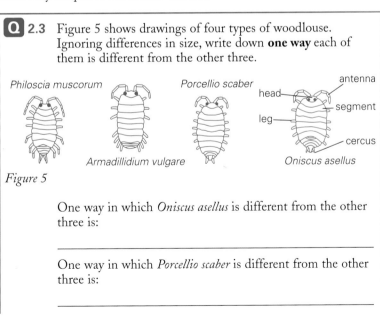

Philoscia muscorum   *Porcellio scaber*   antenna   head   segment   leg   cercus   *Armadillidium vulgare*   *Oniscus asellus*

Figure 5

One way in which *Oniscus asellus* is different from the other three is:

_____

One way in which *Porcellio scaber* is different from the other three is:

_____

One way in which *Armadillidium vulgare* is different from the other three is:

_____

One way in which *Philoscia muscorum* is different from the other three is:

_____

Q 2.4 Here is a more difficult example. Figure 6 shows two scale drawings of the larval stages of a stonefly and a mayfly. These are called **nymphs**.

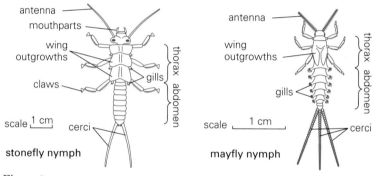

Figure 6

Use the scales to work out the length of each nymph.

Stonefly nymph   _____

Mayfly nymph   _____

Finish the table on the right, listing ten differences between the stonefly nymph and the mayfly nymph. (The first has been done for you.)

	Stonefly nymph	Mayfly nymph
1	Hairless antennae	Hairy antennae
2		
3		
4		
5		
6		
7		
8		
9		
10		

Q 2.5 Now we are going to make some measurements. Look at Figure 7, which shows six examples of measuring instruments.

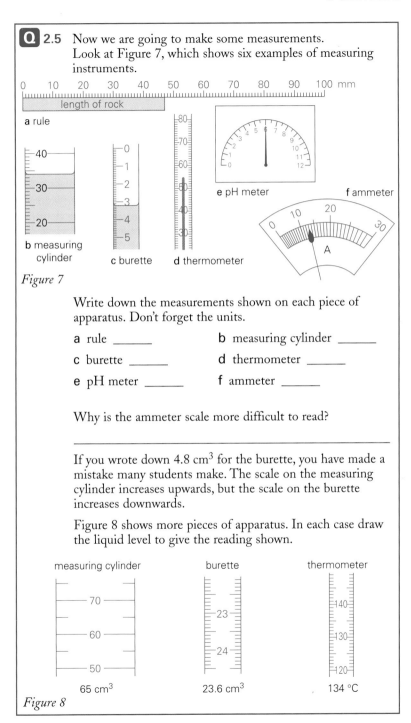

Figure 7

Write down the measurements shown on each piece of apparatus. Don't forget the units.

a rule _____   b measuring cylinder _____

c burette _____   d thermometer _____

e pH meter _____   f ammeter _____

Why is the ammeter scale more difficult to read?

_____

If you wrote down 4.8 cm^3 for the burette, you have made a mistake many students make. The scale on the measuring cylinder increases upwards, but the scale on the burette increases downwards.

Figure 8 shows more pieces of apparatus. In each case draw the liquid level to give the reading shown.

Figure 8

For a mark of 6 or above in Skill Area O you have to repeat readings where necessary. You must always ask yourself if it is possible to repeat the reading *under exactly the same conditions*. If it is not possible, because the situation has changed, write this down and move on. If possible, take sufficient repeat readings and average them and use the average reading when processing your results.

Here are some examples. With a stopclock, girls are timing how long it takes one of them to count from one to 50. Is it worth doing it again and averaging? No, because you are not measuring the same event, so the times can be different. This is an example of where one measurement is right.

Another group of girls is timing how long it takes a pendulum to make 10 swings. Here the experiment can be repeated because the time should always be the same. They are timing the same event. Here are the results.

1st result	2nd result	3rd result	4th result	average
20 seconds	21 seconds	20 seconds	20 seconds	20.25 seconds

Be careful here. Do not assume that the average is more accurate than the original readings. The readings were taken to the nearest second. The average is worked out to the nearest one-hundredth of a second. The average should be written as 20 seconds.

Q 2.6 Let's look at another example. Sarah is investigating the stretchiness of some nylon fishing line. She uses the apparatus shown in Figure 9.

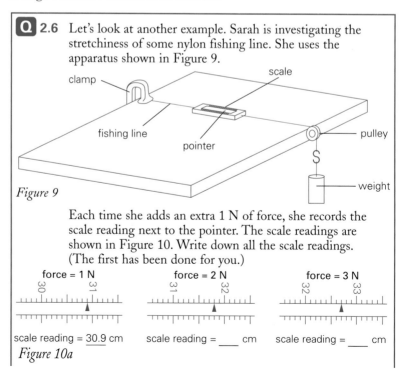

Figure 9

Each time she adds an extra 1 N of force, she records the scale reading next to the pointer. The scale readings are shown in Figure 10. Write down all the scale readings. (The first has been done for you.)

force = 1 N

scale reading = 30.9 cm

force = 2 N

scale reading = ___ cm

force = 3 N

scale reading = ___ cm

Figure 10a

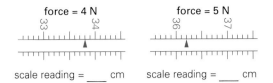

force = 4 N   force = 5 N

scale reading = ____ cm   scale reading = ____ cm

Figure 10b

Now put the results in the table below.

Force/N	Length of fishing line/cm	Extension of fishing line/cm
0	30.0	0.0
1	30.9	0.9
2	____	____
3	____	____
4	____	____
5	____	____

The length of the line at the end of the experiment, with force removed = 30.7 cm. We look at how these results can be processed on page 23.

Q 2.7 Now let us look at a table showing a student's recording of the results of a rate of reaction experiment. In this experiment different volumes of sodium thiosulphate solution and water are mixed. The same volume of dilute hydrochloric acid is added to the different mixtures of sodium thiosulphate solution and water. The time is measured until a cross marked underneath the beaker disappears from view.

Volume of sodium thiosulphate/cm³	Volume of hydrochloric acid/cm³	Volume of water/cm³	Total volume	Time taken for cross to disappear
35	5	15	55	25 sec
5	5	45	55	1.50 min
25	5	25	55	35 sec
10	5	40	55	1 min 15 sec
15	5	30	50 cm³	1 min
45	5	5	55	20 sec

Write down four mistakes in this table.

1 _____

2 _____

3 _____

4 _____

Draw the table out again correctly on the inside back cover of this book. You may find it better not to include one set of results.

Why is it easier to make your conclusion from the new table?

_____

_____

_____

_____

3 Skill Area A

Analysing evidence and drawing conclusions

We will now look at how marks are awarded for analysing evidence and drawing conclusions. It is sometimes possible to get some credit for Skill Area A from the table you produce for Skill Area O. For example, in the sodium thiosulphate, water, hydrochloric acid table you redrew, you should have put the results into an order, e.g. increasing volume of sodium thiosulphate solution. This is processing your results and will give you credit.

Unless you are working at a very low level, scoring only one or two marks for this skill, you can expect to draw a graph for Skill Area A. You are probably used to drawing graphs of mathematical functions, e.g. $y = x^2$ over a range of −5 to +5. You produce a table like the one below.

x	−5	−4	−3	−2	−1	0	+1	+2	+3	+4	+5
y	25	16	9	4	1	0	1	4	9	16	25

You can then plot the graph shown in Figure 11 of the function in the sure knowledge that the value for each point is exactly correct, and that the curve will go through every point. If your curve does not go through a point, it will be because you have not drawn your curve correctly.

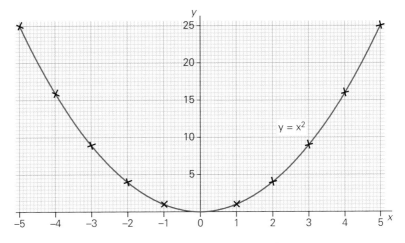

Figure 11

With a scientific graph, the situation is not the same. Every point you have plotted is likely to have some error associated with it. When you draw your curve it may not go through all of the points.

Let us now draw three graphs for the copper, glass and plastic beaker experiment (page 13) on the grid below. Plot the points – it will help you if you use either three different colours or different types of points for copper, glass and plastic. Draw the three curves on your graph. We call these **lines of best fit**. If the points are all on the curve or very close to the curve, this can be used as evidence for the accuracy of the results.

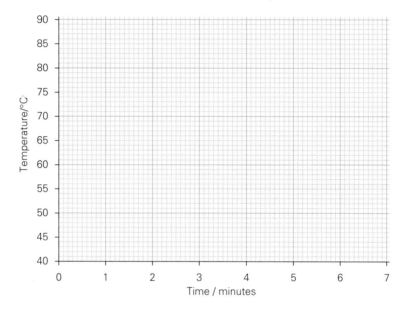

Figure 12

Now let us draw conclusions from this experiment. Looking at your graphs, you have three cooling curves – one for the copper beaker, one for the glass beaker and one for the plastic beaker. Our original prediction was that the copper beaker would cool faster than the glass beaker, and the glass beaker would cool faster than the plastic beaker. The beaker that cools fastest will have the graph which drops most steeply. Certainly, this is the copper beaker. However, the graphs clearly show that the second part of our prediction was wrong. The glass beaker does not cool as quickly as the plastic beaker. Our experiments have shown that our prediction is only partly correct. We will look at this further when we come to Skill Area E. You will notice that the conclusion has been linked back here to the original planning and prediction. This is essential if high marks are to be scored in this Skill Area.

Q 3.1 Look back at the table Sarah got from her experiments stretching some fishing line (page 18). Use the grid in Figure 13 to draw a graph of force applied (on the *x*-axis) against extension (on the *y*-axis). It is usual to put the independent variable (force) on the *x*-axis, and the dependent variable (extension) on the *y*-axis. The first things you have to do are label the axes and choose appropriate scales.

You want to fill as much of the grid as possible. The best scales are:

x-axis –
10 small squares represent 1 N. Each small square represents 0.1 N.

y-axis –
10 small squares represent 1 cm. Each small square represents 0.1 cm.

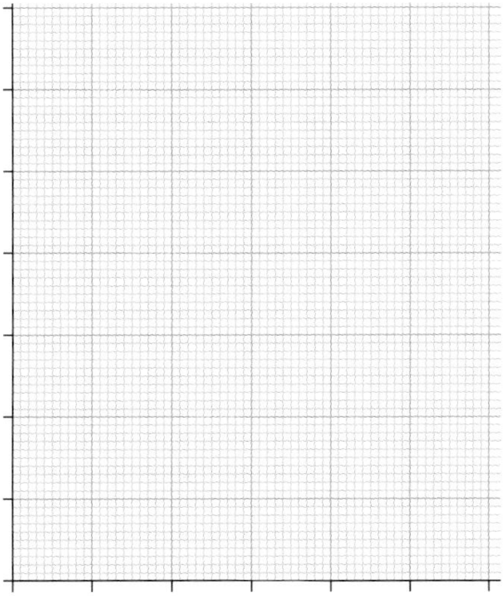

Figure 13

What can you conclude from these results?

_____

_____

Why is it not possible for Sarah to go back and repeat the experiment with the same piece of fishing line?

_____

Can you explain what has happened to the structure of the nylon chains in the line when they have stretched?

_____

_____

If you can answer the last question, you have linked your experimental results with a model of the structure of polymers. This linking is essential for a mark of 7 or 8 in Skill Area P.

4 Skill Area E

Evaluating

Skill Area E is the most difficult skill for you to master. Unlike the other Skill Areas, it is marked out of 6. It involves looking at the results you have obtained and deciding:

- Have I taken enough observations or measurements?
- Have I covered the whole range I am interested in?
- Have I checked my results by repeating them?
- Have I obtained similar results when I repeated them?
- Have I got the right sort of evidence to support my conclusion?
- If I were to repeat the whole experiment, in the light of my experience, how would I try to improve it?

In the experiment with copper, glass and plastic beakers there are other things we should consider:

- Are the beakers the same shape?
- Much of the energy transfer is through the top.
- Is it necessary to put lids on the beakers?
- Are the beakers of the same thickness?

All of these could be included in the evaluation.

Let us consider another experiment, involving photosynthesis in pondweed when it is lit by a lamp. The experiment is carried out using a lamp at different distances from the pondweed, and then with different colours of light produced using filters.

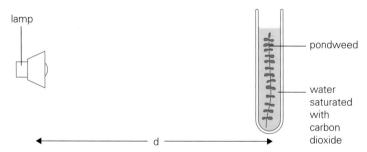

Figure 14

You might find it useful to refer to Letts *GCSE Science Classbook* Units 33–4 and 138 to get some theoretical understanding of the topic of photosynthesis and of filters.

The water is initially saturated with carbon dioxide. Carbon dioxide is used up when photosynthesis takes place. The pondweed is illuminated with the lamp at different distances. The number of bubbles of oxygen formed in two minutes is measured.

A set of results is shown in the table.

Distance from lamp/cm	Number of bubbles in 2 minutes	Average
5	50	
	46	46
	42	
10	40	
	36	36
	32	
15	28	
	24	24
	20	
20	12	
	10	10
	8	

Differently coloured filters are then used and the results shown in the table are obtained. In this experiment the lamp was the same distance from the pondweed in each experiment.

The conclusions drawn by the student are:

1 The rate of photosynthesis is proportional to the amount of light energy.

2 Red and blue light are absorbed better by chlorophyll than green or yellow light.

Colour of light	Number of bubbles formed in 2 minutes
red	31
blue	33
green	1
yellow	24

We are now going to look critically at these results and conclusions. We will try to write an evaluation under two headings.

1 The quality and reliability of the experimental data

You will notice that three results were taken at each distance. However, the results decrease each time. This could be because the solution is saturated with carbon dioxide the first time, but not for the second and third readings. Averaging could be meaningless. What has been used is not an average but the second result each time. Here is a case where repeating the results provides no benefit. You could plot similar graphs using the first or third results in each case.

If the rate of photosynthesis is proportional to the amount of light energy, we should get a straight line when we plot the number of bubbles collected in 2 minutes against some measure of light intensity.

From theory, intensity of light = $\dfrac{1}{d^2}$

Figure 15 is a graph showing the number of bubbles collected in 2 minutes against $\dfrac{1}{d^2}$.

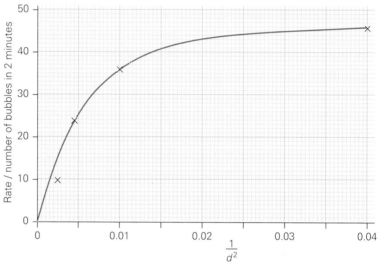

Figure 15

The graph is not a straight line. It resembles the graph on page 71 of Letts *GCSE Science Classbook*. More points are needed to confirm the shape of the graph. As a minimum, values of d of 7.1 cm and 5.8 cm, giving $\dfrac{1}{d^2}$ values of 0.2 and 0.3, are needed.

When differently coloured filters were used, there was no sure knowledge that each filter allowed through the same amount of light. The results confirm the science on page 68 of Letts *GCSE Science Classbook*. Each result was only taken once. Here it would be a benefit to have some more results. It would be necessary, however, to saturate the solution with carbon dioxide each time.

2 Ways in which the experiment could be improved if it was repeated
If the experiment was repeated, a light meter could be used to measure the amount of light hitting the tube containing pondweed.

Sometimes there is criticism of the method of counting bubbles to measure rates. Since the bubbles are usually fairly uniform in size and there are plenty of them, it is more reliable than trying to measure small volumes of gas in a gas syringe.

Q 4.1 Here are some results for the time taken for 10 swings of a pendulum with different lengths of string.

Length of pendulum/cm	Time for 10 swings/s	Time for 1 swing/s
40	12	1.2
80	18	1.8
120	23	2.3

The graph of these results is shown in Figure 16.

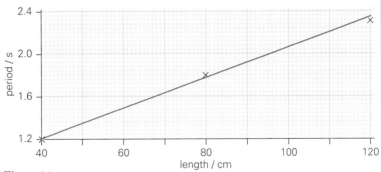

Figure 16

On a separate sheet of paper, write an evaluation of this experiment under two headings:

1 Quality and reliability of the results, and are they enough to support my experiment?

2 Improvements that could be made if the experiment was repeated.

You should now know a great deal about how to carry out Sc1 and should be ready to do some investigations.

5 Writing up your report

The report you write is the only evidence available for comparing you with other students, and for submission to a moderator outside the school. Writing the best possible report you can is obviously very important. This section helps you to do this.

Your report can be handwritten or word processed. If it is handwritten (and most are) write as clearly as possible. Your teacher is used to your handwriting, but this report may be read by people who are not. Often the original report is photocopied, which makes reading it more difficult. If a person has difficulty in reading the report they may miss some important point. A useful tip here is to use a highlighter pen to highlight those points you think are important – the prediction, the conclusion, important points of evaluation. This will draw the attention of the reader to the things that you think are important.

If your report is word processed, it must be word processed by you, and your teacher is required to confirm this. You may use a spell checker, but be careful if you do. A spell checker will tell you that a word you have typed is not in the dictionary in the software, and it will suggest alternatives. You have to choose a suitable alternative that makes sense in the piece you are writing. For example, if you think a compound contains ionic bonding, you might write that the compound is 'ionically bonded'. The spell checker will tell you that 'ionically' does not exist, and will suggest 'ironically' instead. If you choose this alternative, you make your report nonsense.

Your work is marked for spelling, punctuation and grammar by your teacher. Strictly speaking, your whole portfolio of work should have one mark for these, but in practice teachers often mark each piece of work. Spelling, punctuation and grammar only represent about 5% of the mark available for Sc1, but they are marks you do not want to lose. The teacher is directed particularly to your spelling of scientific and technical terms. Read your report carefully and slowly a couple of times before you give it to your teacher. Check the spellings of any words you are uncertain of. Make sure you have written in sentences, with a capital letter at the start and a full stop at the end. Be careful about your use of punctuation marks, especially the apostrophe. There should be few places in a report where an apostrophe can be used.

In some schools and colleges a standard form will be given to you on which to write your report. This is quite acceptable, but sometimes the space given to fill each section may be too much or, more likely, too little. Do not feel restricted by a standard form – use it as a guide. This booklet provides a series of headings for you to follow. You may not choose to use them all, but you should use all of the headings in **bold** type.

Title of investigation

Planning

What I think will happen
This should include a prediction if possible.

Why I think this will happen
This section should include knowledge you have already, and information you have researched in textbooks, databooks, databases, etc. Do not copy out big chunks from a textbook, but write the important points in your own words. Give a reference to your source, e.g. Letts *GCSE Science Classbook*, pages 44–5.

List of the apparatus I plan to use

In order to make my investigation fair, which factors:

■ **affect how the investigation will work?**

■ **will I keep the same and which will I change?**

What will I count and what will I measure?
Decide on the range of measurements you will make, their frequency and the degree of accuracy you can expect from the equipment you are using.

What is my detailed plan?

Any safety issues that will be important.

What preliminary work I have done.

Carrying out the investigation
A detailed account of my experiment.

A record of all observations and measurements made

Your observations should be recorded in a table or chart. Plan the table or chart before you start. Ask your teacher if you are uncertain how to do this.

Were any experiments repeated?

Changes I made to my plan during the investigation

Analysing the results
Are my results presented in a systematic way?

Using my results to produce a pie graph, bar graph, line graph or calculation

What I have found out

Are there any patterns in my results?

Does what I have found out match up with the prediction I made?

Explanation of what happened, using scientific knowledge

Evaluation

How reliable were my results?
Did I take enough measurements, to the correct degree of accuracy, and over an appropriate range?

Are there any results which did not fit the pattern?

If there are, can I explain why these results were obtained?

If I were to repeat the experiment, with the experience I now have, would I do anything differently?

What experiments could I carry out to extend the work I have done?

It is important that you record all of your performances in each Skill Area and in Biology, Chemistry and Physics, as you do not know which experiments will be needed to complete your folio of coursework. The tables on the following pages will help you.

Your final mark

These tables are fairly complicated and must be followed rigidly, even if it means that some of your best marks cannot be used.

Sc2 – Biology	Inv?	Skill Area Mark			
Activity	(yes/no)	P	O	A	E
Chosen mark in skill area					

Sc3 – Chemistry	Inv?	Skill Area Mark			
Activity	(yes/no)	P	O	A	E
Chosen mark in skill area					

Sc4 – Physics	Inv?	Skill Area Mark			
Activity	(yes/no)	P	O	A	E
Chosen mark in skill area					

Double and Single Science

Record the chosen mark from each Skill Area in the Summary Table.

Put a circle around Investigation Marks.

Choose **four** marks to give the best total out of 30 including ...

... 1 mark from each Skill Area

... at least 1 mark from an Investigation

... at least 1 mark from each AT (two of the three for Single Award).

Calculate total mark

Summary Table				
	P	O	A	E
Sc2				
Sc3				
Sc4				
Marks used				

Separate Sciences

Record the chosen mark from each Skill Area in the Summary Table.

Put a circle around Investigation Marks.

Choose **four** marks to give the best total out of 30 including ...

... 1 mark from each Skill Area

... at least 1 mark from an Investigation

... at least 1 mark from two different pieces of work.

Calculate total mark

Sc2 – Biology: Summary Table				
	P	O	A	E
Marks used				

Sc3 – Chemistry: Summary Table				
	P	O	A	E
Marks used				

Sc4 – Physics: Summary Table				
	P	O	A	E
Marks used				

Double Award Science

Your evidence must come from at least three pieces of work. One piece of work must come from Biology (Sc2), one from Chemistry (Sc3) and one from Physics (Sc4). At least one of them must be a whole investigation.

In the table on page 27 you must record the best mark you can in each Skill Area P, O, A and E, making sure that one comes from Sc2, one from Sc3 and one from Sc4, and that one comes from a whole investigation. It is usual to put a circle around the marks for whole investigations.

Single Award Science

Your evidence must come from at least two pieces of work. They must come from two of Biology (Sc2), Chemistry (Sc3) and Physics (Sc4). At least one of them must be a whole investigation.

In the table on page 27 you must record the best mark you can in each Skill Area P, O, A and E, making sure that they come from at least two of Sc2, Sc3 and Sc4, and that one comes from a whole investigation. It is usual to put a circle around the marks for whole investigations.

Separate Sciences

Your evidence in each Science must come from at least two pieces of work in that subject. You must have one mark in each Skill Area. At least one of them must be a whole investigation.

In the table on page 27 you must record the best mark you can in each Skill Area P, O, A and E, making sure that one comes from a whole investigation. It is usual to put a circle around the marks for whole investigations.

Moderation

Your school is required to send off samples of work from different candidates to a Moderator appointed by the Examination Board. The Moderator checks the marking of the work against the criteria to make sure that it is fair.

Providing the marking is fair, he or she will recommend that the marks awarded be used in calculating the final grades. If, however, the marking of your teacher is considered to have been harsh or too generous, your marks may be adjusted.

Only a minority of schools have their marks changed, but *you cannot be certain of the marks that will be used to calculate your grade.*